Tales of the
Anishinaubaek

Mickey + Peggy -
In friendship -
Maxine Noel
iopan mani

Tales of the
Anishinaubaek

Basil H. Johnston

Illustrated by
Maxine Noel *(Ioyan Mani)*

ROM
Royal Ontario Museum

First published in 1993 by the Royal Ontario Museum
100 Queen's Park, Toronto, Ontario M5S 2C6

Managing Editor: Glen Ellis
Designer: Vickie Vasquez-O'Hara

Canadian Cataloguing in Publication Data
Johnston, Basil
  Tales of the Anishinaubaek

ISBN 0-88854-407-3

1. Ojibwa Indians – Legends.   2. Indians of
North America – Legends.   I. Noel, Maxine.
II. Royal Ontario Museum.   III. Title.

E99.C6J64 1993   398.2'089'973   C93-094139-X

Printed and bound in Canada by Friesen Printers

Contents

Introduction

Anishinaubaek (singular Anishinaubae) is an Ojibway word translating literally as "the good beings." It is the name the Ojibway people prefer to call themselves. As yet, there is no standardized spelling, but the pronunciation is generally nish-NAH-bek (singular nish-NAH-bay).

These tales are told by Basil Johnston and Sam Ozawamik. Basil Johnston is an Anishinaubae member of the Cape Croker First Nations Reserve, in Ontario. Sam Ozawamik is an Anishinaubae member of the Wikwemikong First Nations Reserve, in Ontario. The stories were collected and translated from the Anishinaubae by Basil Johnston.

Beyond Yonder

Awuss-woodih

Told by Basil H. Johnston

Translated from the Anishinaubae
by Basil H. Johnston

The following does not apply to just one Anishinaubae, but to all, every single one. There is no question that it is necessary for them to return to the way that they used to worship, to again take up their ancient way of believing. At that time they will survive; they will prosper.

For example, I once came upon a story. Exactly where the story took place is not certain; what is certain is that it was somewhere in Anishinaubae country. It concerns, in particular, the young, two young men in fact.

These Anishinaubaek despised the district where they lived. This land was inordinately desolate. It was rocky. There were no fish and no game. At one point, they voiced their feelings: "It's hard to imagine how poor we are!" All they had to wear were deer hides. Their bows and their canoes were plain.

"Look!" said one of these young men. "It is absolutely beautiful beyond there, to the west, where the sun sets in the evening. The land there must be beautiful. We really ought to migrate there. If our parents will not go, we should just leave on our own."

The people decided to leave. But they had no leader. They therefore chose one of the young men. "You will lead the way," his people told him.

"But I don't know the direction we should follow," he replied.

What was to be expected? This young man knew nothing. He was only fifteen years of age. Nevertheless, he was chosen to be their leader.

Because of his uncertainty the young man went to the water's edge to seek guidance. All of a sudden, a fish broke through the surface, a trout. "What is it that you want?" the trout asked.

"Where we live seems so wretched. It seems much fairer on the far shore, to the west."

"As you wish," the trout replied. "I will take you. First gather your canoes, as many of you as there are. Take everything with you."

The young man at once told his fellow Anishinaubaek. As instructed, the people made small canoes, all of them. Finally, they assembled on the shore. The young man prayed. As if in obedience, the trout, it's said, stuck his head out of the water.

The young Anishinaubae then spoke to this trout: "We're ready; would you take us to where we are going, to that land that is beautiful."

"Very well," said the trout, whereupon he summoned his fellow fish to help him lead the Anishinaubaek.

After a time, they arrived in a different land. It looked wretched. There were no berries and the

14

people were hungry. It was obvious that this wasn't the place. The Anishinaubaek were incensed.

Still farther into the distance the land appeared 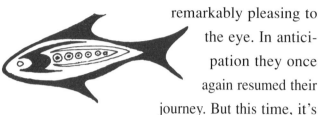 remarkably pleasing to the eye. In antici- pation they once again resumed their journey. But this time, it's said, it was a white fish who guided them to Gauminautikawaeyauk, the Land of Berries, Thunder Bay. But still the land looked the same, poor.

Then, it's said, they asked a fox to take them beyond, to the prairie, Kitchi-mishkodaeng, the Great Prairie. That did not suit the Anishinaubaek either.

By chance, a buffalo came along. He led them all the way to the mountains. After that, some say, it was the mountain goat; mountain goats conduct- ed the Anishinaubaek across the mountains, to the Pacific. But even that land did not seem right for the Anishinaubaek.

On they journeyed, toward the north, it's said, where dwell the white bears and where also live the seals. But it was hardly fit. To the sight it was barren.

At last they met Nanabush. "Where are you going?" he asked.

"Oh, we are looking for that beautiful land where the wild animals abound—deer, rabbits, moose, fish—where fish are abundant, and berries as well.

"Why, where you have come from it is thus," said Nanabush.

That being the case, they came back, these people, and when they were once more at home they saw that what Nanabush had said was indeed true. It might seem that it was for nothing that they had wandered so far abroad, but it is said that not until they returned to it did they cherish their own land.

In Times Past

Ikoh

Told by Sam Ozawamik

Collected and translated from the
Anishinaubae by Basil H. Johnston

 At one time the Anishinaubaek knew about such matters as where the mermaids might be. Perhaps these mermaids lived in Little Wikwemikong. They might have been seen surfacing.

A young Anishinaubae man was warned: "Don't go over there!"

For whatever reason, he apparently didn't. Then on one occasion when he was hunting, he happened to come by that place.

And he saw women in the distance—they were naked—frolicking in the water, near the beach. "Oh, so this is it," he said to himself, "what I have been warned about!"

From there he stared at them. "What can they be doing?" he must have wondered. He tried to get closer. Closer still he went, secretly.

Among the cavernous rocks—you know this place—he approached them. He got out of the water and crept toward them. From close up he would see these nude women.

Suddenly, he leaped upon and seized one of them. Immediately he was swallowed by the water. He clung to that woman, but she dove deep and vanished.

There was nothing further. It is unlikely that he told anyone about it, or went back there.

Much later, though, a year having elapsed, he thought about the mermaids again. "I'm going back," he said. "Hiyauh! They are there still!"

As before, he came upon them, but they fled. One, however, did not take flight; she remained seated, away from the others. So he went to see her. As he suspected, she was cradling her infant. She must have conceived when he had held her. Something he must have done to her, a year before. Such is life.

"Well, come along with me," he invited her, "to my parents' home."

Somewhere near where they made their home he left her. "Wait here for a while," he cautioned. Having no alternative, he asked his mother for clothing.

"What are you going to do with it?" she asked.

"I'm going to bring a young woman home," he answered. "She's wearing nothing."

"That is precisely why you have always been forbidden to go there!" said his mother. "Still you went!"

Reluctantly, she gave him a tattered sheet. He dressed the girl in it and brought her home, the child as well.

Somewhat later on it began to thunder. They were unusually afraid. "The thunders are coming," they said. The young woman seemed to disappear. They looked everywhere for her, but she was gone.

A bit later on, when the storm had subsided, she reappeared.

"Where did you go?" they asked.

"Oh, yes!" she answered, "to the second level of this earth."

"Listen," they warned her, "you are not to make off again."

Well, later on it thunderstormed. There is no doubt 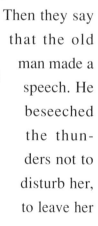 that she was afraid. For that reason he held her, that man.

Then they say that the old man made a speech. He beseeched the thunders not to disturb her, to leave her alone. Then there came, from out of this world, thunder fire, falling fire, a very intense thunder-storm. In spite of all of this, she survived.

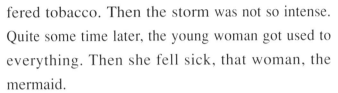

When it resumed thundering the old man performed a ritual. He offered tobacco. Then the storm was not so intense. Quite some time later, the young woman got used to everything. Then she fell sick, that woman, the mermaid.

Not long after that, she invited her man to accompany her; they were to visit the place she had come from. They at once set out; they entered the waters. Step by step he went deeper into the water. Soon he was submerged. It must be supposed that he dove under.

It looks just like this. It probably resembled our world.

After a time, they arrived where the old people, her parents, dwelled. Her father was not pleased: "'Don't go over there!' I tried to tell you. 'Don't go over there!' Now you have brought this spirit."

For some time he lived with his in-laws there, under the water. It seems also that there were strangers, those living outside the community, who decided that they would enter into a contest with the men. Although it was clear to the young man that he might die in that strange place, he was not worried in the least.

Preparations were made for the contest, beginning with a playing field in which a metal stake was standing. The men were to throw metal balls and strike this great stake. As each of them hit it the stake bent. Finally, it was the Anishinaubae's turn.

He likewise struck the target. Then there was awesome fire, forming a chain. He broke that stave; he shattered it.

The people fled. No one remained. Even his own father-in-law ran away.

"What is wrong with them?" his wife asked.

Later on, the old people came back, along with his other in-laws. Some did not come close, so afraid were they. Perhaps that Anishinaubae was in nature like the thunders. They fasted in those days; the people fasted. At one time they were blessed with the good will of the thunders. Some were. Perhaps this man was one of them.

Following this, the Anishinaubae and his mermaid came away; they returned to this world. They never went back.

The mermaid is not far from here. I heard that a long time ago. They say it was a mermaid, a woman scaled from the waist down, that the Anishinaubae married. It was supposed to have happened. They used to see her over at Little Wikwemikong. It most likely did happen. At one time the Anishinaubaek were endowed with supernatural powers. That is why such things happened to them.

The Shining Plant

Waussauh-gunushk

Told by Sam Ozawamik

Collected and translated from the
Anishinaubae by Basil H. Johnston

 One time, they say, there was a man living outside a village somewhere. He had a wife, as is natural. When she died, he prepared her body. After this, he left that place. His life there was finished. He left. "I will go fetch her now," he resolved.

How long he wandered is uncertain. Where he might have gone is anyone's guess. Eventually, he came to a place where there was an old man. "I knew that you were coming. I waited for you," said the old man. "She passed by here—her—your woman. She spoke as to intimidate me, made every effort to do so. But, no, I did not transform her into that state of being that those who have died enter."

The old man had waited for this Anishinaubae. He knew that the man would be searching for his wife.

"Here is the situation," he said. "There will be a celebration, a cheerful celebration, and you will catch her. You will take her with you." Afterwards, he was carefully instructed as to what he was to do. Later, at the festival, he caught her.

A plant known as Father Spectre, or Rabbit Spectre, is supposed to have been the Shining Plant. Perhaps this little grass was a globe in form; it might have been hollow. And that is where he put that woman. But really it was her spirit he put there. That is where she would dwell.

"She will be very demanding, very vociferous, this woman," the old man continued. "'Ah! I beg you, release me,' and similar sentiments will she express. But don't you dare set her loose, not until you are instructed. In due course you will be informed of everything."

And so he gathered herbs and learned medicine that he was to apply to his woman's eyes. But he was taking much too long. Her eyes were failing.

He was also learning what he was to feed her. He was not to feed her a full meal, only a little of this soup. He was instructed well by the old man. "In addition, I will assist you in every way," he counseled. "You will carry with you a small amount of this; where you will be going is far."

The man left. He camped overnight along the way. Without success the woman cried out: "I beg you let me go. I bring you hardship, don't you see, as you carry me!"

"You are not at all heavy," the man replied. Soon enough he set her down.

"I'm also cold," she shivered. "Please! Open up! I will cook for you, and I will make tea for you!"

Eventually, he arrived at a place where there was a burial hut, a burial hut made of skin. Someone was interred there. And that is where he was shown what to do.

Finally, he made an opening and released her. She was heard to speak: "Who is it that would reincarnate me? No one who is alive ought to be so confined."

He spoke to her. He made medicine for her eyes; he healed her eyes. He administered more medicine to her; he warmed her so that she would recover. Under the medication she got better.

They left. Where they went is unknown.

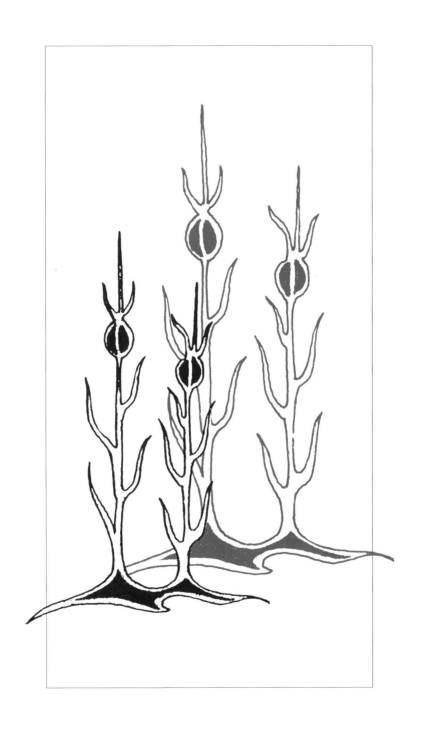

Thunders

Animikeek

Told by Sam Ozawamik

Collected and translated from the
Anishinaubae by Basil H. Johnston

And he spoke to the thunders. At least, that is what one man told me. It was during the time of boiling down maple sap in the spring. This man did not go. He was sick. It was impossible for him to work. All the elders had gone. Only this man was left.

While he sat in his house someone came to visit him. "Hello," said the visitor. "I've come to take you with me. We want you to come and help us."

"Well, I'm really in no condition to go anywhere," said the man. I'm barely alive."

"There's nothing wrong with you," replied the visitor. "I've come to take you with me. I've got good reason to invite you to come with me." The visitor wouldn't stop talking to him.

"Alright, then," said the man, "I'll go."

(In fact, the visitor had invited him for the purpose of killing someone.)

The man got to his feet and took up his bow. Then the visitor instructed him: "Wherever I step, you step also. Do everything that I do."

"Accordingly," recalled the man, "I followed him. Step for step."

In no time they were borne aloft and taken to the firmament. That is where the thunders must abide. On they went. Eventually, they came to some place that was exceedingly distant. In fact, this place was supposed to be Baushkidauwung, the Place of Thunders. A deity is said to dwell there. But he is not benevolent. He destroys people. Always. As it turned out, it was none other than this deity they were supposed to capture.

Well, they tried to strike him but the arrow only glanced off, falling into the midst of trees. Obviously, the task was impossible. Then, in an instant, the earth cleaved open. They shot him, this bad spirit, or whatever he was. In fact, he was a snake. The deed was done; they had slain him.

Another man who was there suggested that the visitor should take the man back to where he had found him. "Take him back," he advised. "He's served us well." So it was.

Finally, this spirit visitor instructed the man: "Look to see which direction I go. Look my way." But the spirit vanished and the man lost sight of him. All the man could find was a small feather lying there. A small feather. A very small feather indeed. It may have been this spirit visitor. He picked it up, put it into his pocket. How good it made him feel. He was well again. There was no explaining it.

So he decided to visit his father. As he approached, he was sighted by his father's friends.

They were sure they were looking at a ghost. "It's a spectre," they said. "Since he was very sick, he must have died. It can't be him; it must be his ghost." As he approached, they were afraid.

So he told them his story, told them what had happened. After that he cut wood, felled many trees. He had his strength back. It was the thunders who had helped him. And that is how the Anishinaubaek came to understand the thunders.

On another occasion, it was a woman who was addressed by them, told to go with them. She was fully instructed as to what she was to do. It was a man who spoke to her. "You must go there, and there you must sit. Someone will arrive there. It is that person whom the thunders wish to capture."

As instructed, the woman went there. As predicted, a man arrived while she was sitting. He was very striking. The woman received her guest and visited him. She brushed his hair down. Soon, she lulled him to sleep. She did as she had been instructed by the one who had spoken to her.

The woman then took his head from her lap. Then she left. On her way down she saw a cloud suspended in air. In that instant, something sounded . . . thunders.

They captured the spirit, that man-spirit. To them he resembled a human being. And, as may have been required, they took him to the thunders. And that is his status. He is a prisoner of the thunders.

I heard of another man, a medicine man out west. Young Bear is what he was called. It was he who summoned the thunders. "Thunder Spirits," he called. "They will come into our midst," he said. It was none other than an Anishinaubae who summoned them.

But this, no one will believe! There was a woman at Cape Croker. Bessie . . . Bessie King. This was quite some time ago. She spoke of events that had occurred at some distance from the village. She spoke of her grandmother in particular. It had been a common practice for her to offer tobacco; whenever it thundered, it's said, she never failed to put tobacco into the ground, or into the fire.

But one time she forgot to. Then, the thunders stopped and lingered. There they remained above her. They called out loudly. "Oh!" she said. "I forgot tobacco!" So she called upon a girl. "Run and take this tobacco, take it into the garden and bury it there."

The little girl ran with the tobacco. She set it in the ground and ran back. Immediately, a ball of fire fell to the earth at that place. The thunders were appeased. Without delay they moved on.

Medicine Woman

Mashki-aki-quaewuk

Told by Sam Ozawamik

Collected and translated from the
Anishinaubae by Basil H. Johnston

According to legend, there was a woman suffering from something. She was unwell. She lived somewhere, alone really, except for her sister. Apparently, her sister was always counselling her. If something in her condition were to change, she advised, she would have to leave forthwith. Even if she were to forget something, she should not bother with it. That's how it should be. Just leave.

Naturally enough, this woman caught something. As she had been told to, she left quickly. By chance, she forgot her string thread, something to sew with. She took a moment to run back to fetch it. As she arrived she felt something. Her condition had worsened. She told her sister.

"Well, I did try to tell you," her sister scolded. "'Don't go back,' I said to you. But you came back anyway. What's done is done. You've bungled things with your foolishness."

Another time, there was a certain man who was like a wendigo. He ate human beings. Just as quickly as his bones moved, he devoured humans. Of course, people were terrified.

On one occasion, he appeared when the men were away hunting. "What will we do?" the women asked. "He will slay all of us for sure, this one. And, besides, other humans must be very far away.

A hundred miles perhaps. It would take someone a long time to get there, to tell what is happening."

At last, one woman volunteered. It must be assumed that all of them fasted, including this woman. A dog offered to guide her. So she ran off, as fast as she could go.

Astounding! She ran a hundred miles. "We are being killed," she reported. "One of our men caught something, that's what's happened to him."

The men left at once and arrived before morning. They captured him; they captured the wendigo. He was unbelievably tough, and strong. They tried without success to cut off his head, but the head flew back into its place. Even though he was beheaded, his head flew back into position. He was like ice. Even though he was struck, it was useless. He was as hard as ice.

Eventually, they managed to kill him, by ganging up on him as it were. They seized and held onto his head in particular. In the end, they managed to kill him. By such means did they survive. Such was the medicine power of that woman. In a sense, she achieved this alone.

There was another person who had a sore leg, both legs in fact. Rheumatism, that's what he had. They say there was something special about this one woman. This man went to her, and they made a

hole in his leg. They tried divining, but they found nothing. According to the story, this medicine woman put her hand into the opening. Then she held his leg right here, at the upper thigh. Then the other leg. When she touched them his legs swelled. Then the swelling came down. He got better. His rheumatism went away. He must be walking now. All because that woman touched him.

So filled with medicine power was woman in earlier times.

Snowmaker

Gaupoonikae

Told by Sam Ozawamik

Collected and translated from the
Anishinaubae by Basil H. Johnston

As regards one Anishinaubae, he was in the habit of contesting with a certain winter spirit. In all likelihood this being was called Snowmaker.

That Anishinaubae lived in a small house, a mud hut. It was snowing, according to accounts, and he had put wood into the fire. Then he brought more wood into the house. He was competing with Snowmaker. They were contending.

After a while, the man was unable to pry open his door in order to go out. It was hopeless. The snow was too deep. He was no longer able to move that door. That was the situation. However, he had more firewood in that place. He settled down, lay there. Once in a while, he added wood to his fire.

By now, this Anishinaubae was hungry. In fact, he had a craving for rabbit meat. Apparently, there was an immense rabbit available to the Anishinaubaek in this area, ready for eating. Moreover, the rabbit was soaked in fat. The Anishinaubaek stored this fat for future use. It seems that rabbit fat gives off a particularly strong flame.

This Anishinaubae also had a small lunch with him. Everything he needed was in it. Hauh! He put

more wood into the fire. The storm was unbeliev-
able. In due time his little house was going to be
buried by snow!

He stayed by his chimney. His pile of firewood
was growing smaller and smaller. "This is it!" he
thought to himself. The woodsmoke was barely
going out. There would be no other chance. He was
going to be buried to death by snow!

What else could be expected? After all, they
were warring, he and Snowmaker. Still, he put
more wood into the fire. Very little was left. He was
also running short of food. Soon he would have
only his jar of rabbit fat.

It became impossible to go on any longer. There
was no other choice. He poured that rabbit fat into
the fire. In the next instant it burst into flame. In a
short while, a hole was burned through above. Ho!
The snow melted. He poured on more rabbit fat.
Next thing, the snow was burned through entirely.

Then, someone in the distance was heard to say:
"Ah! Really you beat me!" He was heard to speak,
that Snowmaker, according to legend.

How long they had battled is uncertain. Two
days or perhaps even three. It was none other than
an Anishinaubae who challenged Snowmaker, who-
ever Snowmaker might have been. He might be
Nanabush, or he who made winter.

Spies

Geemootaugaedjig

Told by Sam Ozawamik

Collected and translated from the
Anishinaubae by Basil H. Johnston

In the late winter some of the Anishinaubaek were making maple sugar. Others had gone hunting.

Apparently, a man had killed a bear. The man and his wife cooked this bear, and then the woman stirred the fat in a cauldron, a huge cauldron, they say. As she stirred, she saw a shadow cast upon the surface of the fat in her cauldron. A man was watching her. His image was clearly mirrored. He had come to look at her. Such persons as this are spies. They come to observe, perhaps to murder.

At once, she called her husband. "Just look at this," she said to him quietly, so as not to be heard." It's said that he in fact saw the man's image there, saw the spy.

He then took up his bow. "This is what I did when I shot the bear," he announced to his wife. "'I'm set. Take your time,' I said to myself." First, he bent his bow in simulated aim in another direction, then wheeled around suddenly and shot the spy. The ground shook with the sound of others running away.

The others who had been away hunting came back at about this time. One of them had seen those who had run away. Next morning, the spies were attacked at dawn. Again they fled. They threw their

possessions into bundles and escaped to the place where their friends were.

Farther on, the man who had been shot collapsed. He eventually died. The arrow had gone into his chest. To avoid detection his companions cut off his head so that he could not be recognized. They also skinned him. He must be lying there still, his head cut off. They made off with his head.

Meanwhile, other Anishinaubaek were making maple sugar. There was a woman stirring the boiling syrup; she was making maple sugar candy. At the same time, this man was lying down; actually he was lying down near a wall. It's said that he was lurking and spying. As he looked upon this woman, he was smitten by her looks. "I will steal the affections of that woman," he is supposed to have said. Still, his real purpose was to spy. "Go, look about," was what he had been instructed to do. He most certainly must have been spying up to the time that he saw this woman. There is no denying that he wanted her. "I'll win her affections," he vowed to himself, "and if I have to I'll kill that man with her. I will own her."

She continued stirring. Then the spy burst into the house and set upon her husband who was lying down. The intruder grabbed him by the neck. At the same time, the woman broke off some thick maple syrup. It was like a rope. Then she lashed the spy's back with that. He must have been naked, that man. She struck him along the length of his back. Then she broke off some more syrup rope and lashed him again. His back was burned by now. So she broke off some more and thrashed him again. Almost as a reflex his arms whipped back. He let go of her husband and bolted.

Not long after, the men came to this place, the sugar bush. Luckily, the spy had left a trail. They found him lying on the ground. He had died, most likely burned across his back by that syrup rope.

Another group had a somewhat similar experience. Two children, a boy and a girl, were eating. A man peeped through a hole at them. This person had been hired as a spy. "For our safety," he had been instructed, "check up on those people over there. Count them. They are to be attacked in the morning. At that time they will be killed."

The little girl was then supposed to have said, "I will put this food away and eat it tomorrow." She would save some of this meal for the future. The spy looked especially upon this little girl. He was exceedingly heartsick. His own daughter was similar to this one. It was she he was remembering. Apparently, he was very fond of his little daughter. He was heartsick that these children were in danger.

As a result, he took pity on them. He went inside. "This is why I've come in," he said. "I have a daughter the same size as you. I love her. Now, over there is a hollow, a gully. Go in that direction as you run away."

It was settled. The children quickly got ready during the night. They went along the ravine as they had been instructed. There was no one lying in ambush. Very early in the morning, the assassins arrived. No one was there; the place was empty. The spy was questioned. "How can this be explained?" they asked. "You didn't tell anything by any chance, did you?"

"Of course not!" he replied. "Why should I do such a thing?"

They did not believe him. In fact, they were ready to kill him. "Some are remarkably capable," he argued. "They probably knew beforehand."

At that, they left. "It's better that we don't stay. We ought to go directly. They'll be here in a short while. Then they'll kill us!" At that point, they fled.

These were scarers of beasts.

Snake Spirit

Mishi-ginaebig

Told by Sam Ozawamik

Collected and translated from the
Anishinaubae by Basil H. Johnston

 A young woman was warned: "Don't you dare go over there. There is a lake there. You will not go over there."

For a long time she didn't. Then one day, when she was alone, keeping the lodge, she asked herself, "Why can't I go there, anyway? It doesn't matter; I *will* go." She was careful not to let anyone know where she had gone.

When she got there she saw a man, a handsome man. "It's obvious why I wasn't allowed to come here," she thought. "This is the reason."

After a while, she conceived. But only when she grew big did it become known where she had been. "Well, well," they said to her, "even though you were warned, you visited that spirit." They say that spirit was a snake called "adder." A great, huge snake.

At length she gave birth to a child, two children, actually, a boy and a girl. However, they were unusually cross. Ahauh! They were spirits, and for this reason that woman could not stay in the village.

They took her somewhere. She was given nothing; she was merely released, together with her children.

Somehow, they managed to survive. The children grew up. Perhaps the young man worked along with his sister and his mother. In due course, they prospered. In time they grew into greater numbers. These were the Iroquois, the little Iroquois. They were said to be more than unusually bad tempered. But what was expected? They were spirits.

That's what I used to hear.

Mermaid

Nebaunaubaequae

Told by Sam Ozawamik

Translated from the Anishinaubae
by Basil H. Johnston

Let's turn to the mermaid. Two young men went fishing off a point. They camped there for the night. After midnight, one of these Anishinaubaek announced to his companion that he would check their nets. He set out, paddling. But he did not return. Nor was his boat found.

The Anishinaubae who survived was accused. "You did something to him," they said.

One winter elapsed. He was to be tried by his fellow Anishinaubaek. They repeated: "You most certainly did something to your fellow being. You must now take your own life."

To make his point, the young man went to his friend's parents. "I did nothing to him," he pleaded. "I have no idea where he might have gone. The last time that I saw him, he was going to check the nets. That is what really happened," he told them.

But it was of no use. "It must be you, only you," they said. "You must go to the same place; you will drown yourself there."

So, apparently, that is where he went. There on the shore he wondered about the fate of his friend. "I'm unjustly treated for nothing," he said to himself. "I didn't do anything to my friend. He just vanished. Like that!"

While the young Anishinaubae sat there, his friend emerged from the water.

"Hello," he said. "They've allowed me to come to visit my fellow Anishinaubaek and my parents."

"But who are 'they,'" his friend asked, "and where did you go?"

"When I set out to check the nets," he explained, "a woman watched me from the water. A mermaid. My canoe sank at once. Then I was carried away under water by the current. It was this woman who took me. But she was reluctant to bring me to where her parents lived. So she concealed me somewhere. In time, she was found out.

"'Why did you bring that man here?' they asked her.

"'Because I found him attractive,' she answered.

"'You shouldn't have brought him here. Humans, the Anishinaubaek, mistreat us. However, it's much too late for you to take him back. He's dead, no doubt about it.'"

So they got married and had children. But these children appeared different from other children. In time the man became lonesome. He yearned once more to see his parents and to tell them where he was.

"Alright," the merpeople said to him. "You will be allowed to go if you bring back tobacco, a good quantity of tobacco. We lack the stuff. Since we've been here the Anishinaubaek never think of us. They offer tobacco to deities in every other quarter.

But for those of us in these waters—nothing! Actually, they offer tobacco at Boweting, but for those of us abiding near the shores they make no offering."

"Done!" he told them. "I will bring tobacco."

On that condition he was released.

Together, the two Anishinaubaek went to where the others camped. When they saw the missing man, they regarded him with profound wonder. When he explained where he had been, they did not believe him.

Then the other one said, "See, I did not do anything to him. It was not on my account that he drowned." At last they believed him.

For a time his friend lingered, visiting his parents. The Anishinaubaek helped him collect tobacco, a great quantity of it, which he was to deliver to the people of the waters. Before he left, he instructed them: "You also will offer tobacco, and the deities will be appeased, and they will be contented, as will the underwater mermen and mermaids. Now, then, I must go."

The Anishinaubaek were disconsolate. Then one night the young man left for the point in the distance. From there he swam to the middle of the lake. Then he vanished. Down into the depths he swam with the great tobacco offering, which he delivered to the principal water spirit there. These spirits were also able to make offerings of tobacco, and also smoke. By such means they were able to overcome other spirits that were hostile to them.

Soon enough, this young man, young mer-man, became a father again. He fathered many mer-children, girls and boys. Only a long time after, though, did he remember his parents.

One time, it's said, he sensed something, and it was only then that he remembered them. Of course he had to ask permission of the principal spirit there. "Would you permit me to go to see them, for they too will leave their earthly home."

Reluctantly, he was allowed to go, allowed only on the condition that he take his wife and children also.

One time, the old man and woman were down at the shore. Their thoughts were about their son who had lost his life in that water. Just then he surfaced. They surfaced.

"Sam, look!" said the old woman. "Little mer-men and mermaids!"